FRED BASSET YEARBOOK 2017

Copyright © Alex Graham Limited, 2016

Drawings by Michael Martin

All rights reserved.

No part of this book may be reproduced by any means,
nor transmitted, nor translated into a machine language,
without the written permission of the publishers.

Condition of Sale
This book is sold subject to the condition that it shall not,
by way of trade or otherwise, be lent, resold, hired out or otherwise
circulated in any form of binding or cover other than that in which it
is published and without a similar condition including this condition
being imposed on the subsequent purchaser.

Summersdale Publishers Ltd
46 West Street
Chichester
West Sussex
PO19 1RP
UK

www.summersdale.com

Printed and bound in the Czech Republic

ISBN: 978-1-84953-913-5

Today I'm thinking outside the box!

Substantial discounts on bulk quantities of Summersdale books are available to corporations, professional associations and other organisations.
For details contact Nicky Douglas by telephone: +44 (0) 1243 756902, fax: +44 (0) 1243 786300 or email: nicky@summersdale.com.

WELL, DO YOU WANT TO GO TO THE CINEMA OR NOT, DEAR?

What a silly idea. It's cold and pouring with rain! It would be much more sensible to stay at home in the warm and keep me company...

UMMM...?

But that's just my humble opinion!

Huh! Well, there's not much here for me!

A rather limited larder!

HAPPY BIRTHDAY, AMANDA!

Who's a clever boy, then?!

OH, FRED! YOU'RE SOAKED TO THE SKIN!

YOU MUST BE FREEZING! QUICK, DEAR, GET A NICE WARM TOWEL FROM THE AIRING CUPBOARD!

PUT HIS BED BY THE FIRE, DEAR, AND BRING HIM HIS DINNER, WOULD YOU...

I'm really going to milk this!

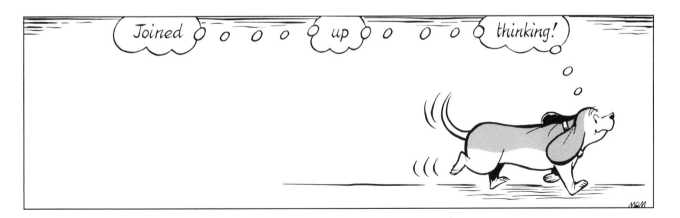

Mobile phone + computer

+ television =

Boredom!!

Little Mia is very good at abstract art —

She's a dab hand at it!

It was ages ago that I dug up the vegetables!

My custody time limit must have expired by now!

I'VE JUST BEEN TRIMMING OUR HEDGE, JIM. WOULD YOU LIKE ME TO TRIM UP YOURS WHILE I'M HERE?

THAT WOULD BE NICE OF YOU. ARE YOU SURE YOU DON'T MIND?

NO, NO—OF COURSE NOT!

Mind? Of course he doesn't mind—

He's been dying to have a go at it for ages!

Canine Salon

High maintenance!

Danny?

So it is...

Well spotted!

Early morning walks in the long grass...

...make me dewy-eyed!

YOU WOULDN'T BELIEVE WHAT SORT OF DAY I'VE HAD!

OH, ME TOO!

BOB WAS OFF SICK, SO I HAD HIS WORKLOAD TO DEAL WITH!

THE WASHING MACHINE LEAKED ALL OVER THE FLOOR!

THEN WE HAD A MASSIVE COMPUTER GLITCH!

I HAD TO TAKE ANGELA TO THE HOSPITAL—SHE SPRAINED HER ANKLE BADLY!

Losing my ball pales into insignificance, I guess?!

JOAN HAS CERTAINLY GOT HER HANDS FULL —

I'VE TRIED A NEW RECIPE THIS EVENING, DEAR!

Prepare for the worst...

TA-DA!

...and hope for the best!

Phew! I don't know about you, lads, but I could do with a lie down—

This seems like an ideal spot!

Taffy certainly has style—

Freestyle!

OH, FRED — WHAT A MESS!

I can't stop now—

Work in progress!

Well, that's that then!

Rather short-lived but I shall just have to accept it!

What's gone is gone!

FRED

Mmm...biscuits!

Ooops! Silly me—

I'm rather accident prone!

A job well done!